This curious model is a three-di[mensional] [...] of magic square called 'diabolic' or [...] in a truly remarkable number of way[s...] [m]agic squares, see pages 2 & 3 of the [...]

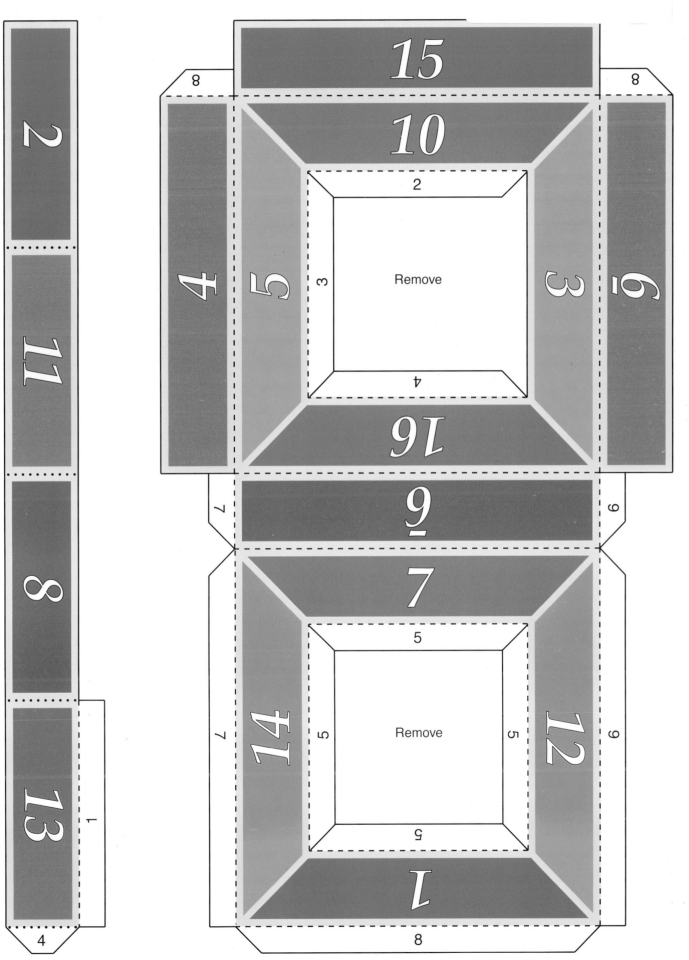

THE DIABOLIC
FRAME

8

8

4

8

5

4

6

1

7

5

3

6

7

5

2

5

FOLDING AND UNFOLDING CUBES

Eight small cubes are linked together in a rather clever way to make this curious model. It can be transformed from one shape to another in a seemingly endless progression, so displaying different motifs and colours. See also page 5 of the minibook.

The other pieces of this model are on page 5.

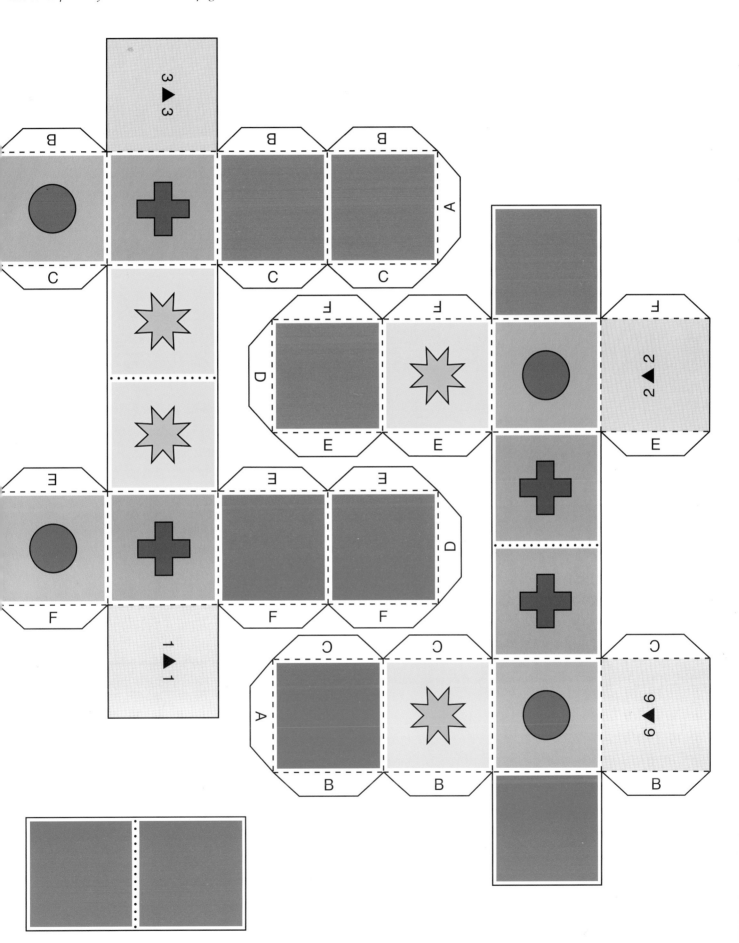

FOLDING AND UNFOLDING CUBES

B
B B
A
F
F F
C C
C
E
D
E E
E E
E
C
C C
D
F F
F
A
B B
B
1 ▲ 1
2 ▲ 2

The other pieces of this model are on page 3.

F E

C B

5 ▲ 5

7 ▲ 7

F E

C B

F E

C B

D

A

A

D

B C

E F

B C

E F

4 ▲ 4

8 ▲ 8

B C

E F

A

D

B

C E

F

B

C E

F

B

C

E

F

3 ▲ 3

4 ▲ 4

5 ▲ 5

7 ▲ 7

6 ▲ 6

8 ▲ 8

F

E

C

B

F

E C

B

F

E

C

B

D

A

Use these models to investigate the curious properties that Möbius strips have. Make all six by glueing corresponding letters together (matching the ▲s) and then cut along the white lines drawn on two of them. Glue each of the sliding labels around its own corresponding strip. These labels draw attention to their special features. For more information, see pages 8 & 9 of the minibook.

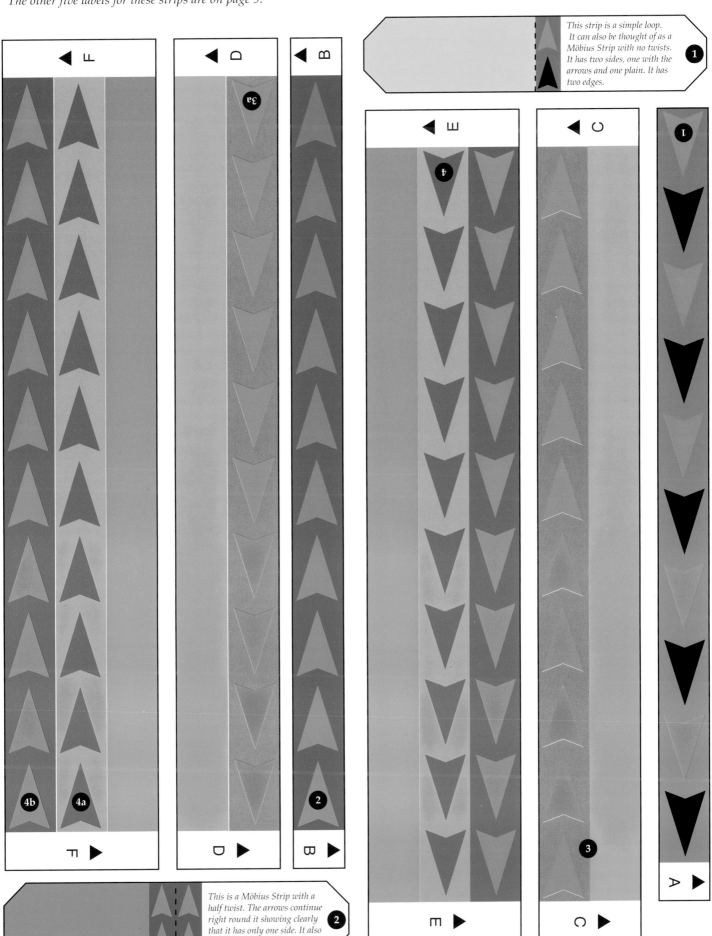

This strip is a simple loop. It can also be thought of as a Möbius Strip with no twists. It has two sides, one with the arrows and one plain. It has two edges. **1**

This is a Möbius Strip with a half twist. The arrows continue right round it showing clearly that it has only one side. It also has a single edge. **2**

MOBIUS MISCELLANY

Cut out these pieces when facing page 7.

Glue blue areas together around Strip.

Label for Möbius Strip **1**

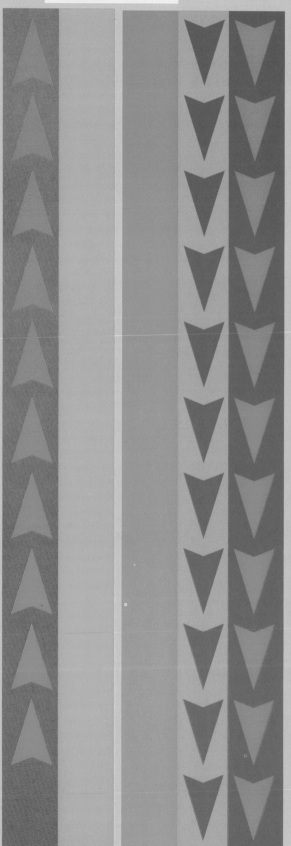

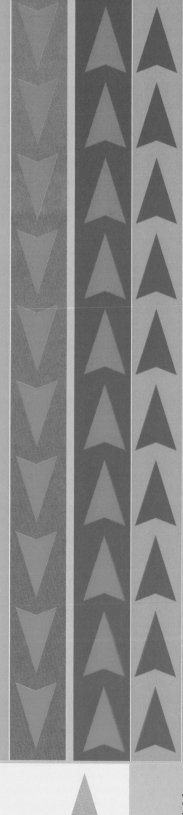

Glue blue areas together around Strip.

Label for Möbius Strip **2**

The other pieces of this miscellany are on page 7.

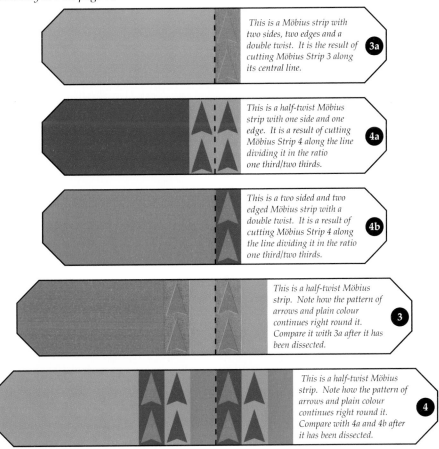

3a This is a Möbius strip with two sides, two edges and a double twist. It is the result of cutting Möbius Strip 3 along its central line.

4a This is a half-twist Möbius strip with one side and one edge. It is a result of cutting Möbius Strip 4 along the line dividing it in the ratio one third/two thirds.

4b This is a two sided and two edged Möbius strip with a double twist. It is a result of cutting Möbius Strip 4 along the line dividing it in the ratio one third/two thirds.

3 This is a half-twist Möbius strip. Note how the pattern of arrows and plain colour continues right round it. Compare it with 3a after it has been dissected.

4 This is a half-twist Möbius strip. Note how the pattern of arrows and plain colour continues right round it. Compare with 4a and 4b after it has been dissected.

THE SQUARE ROTATING RING

This curious model will rotate for ever through its centre forming and reforming a square outline in a most satisfactory way. For its net and further information about its angles, see page 15 of the minibook.

The other piece of this model is on page 11.

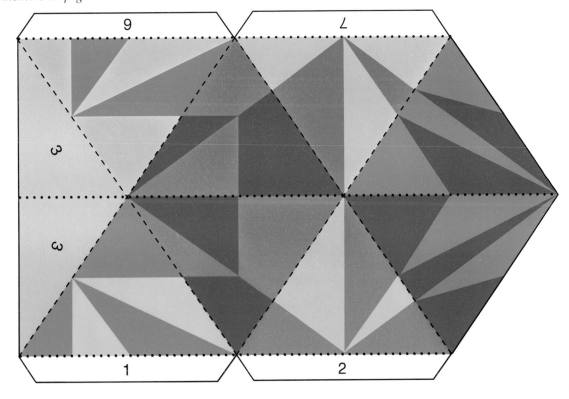

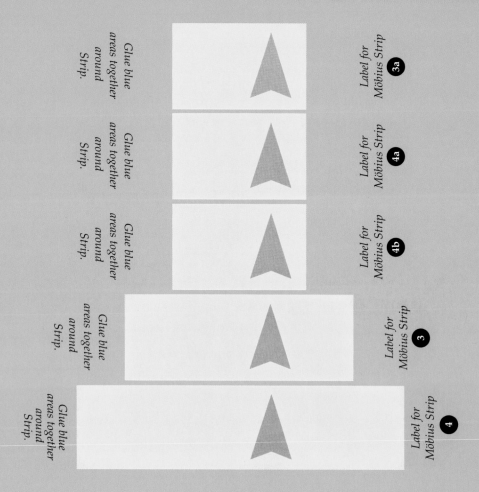

Glue blue areas together around Strip.

Glue blue areas together around Strip.

Glue blue areas together around Strip.

Glue blue areas together around Strip.

Glue blue areas together around Strip.

Label for Möbius Strip **3a**

Label for Möbius Strip **4a**

Label for Möbius Strip **4b**

Label for Möbius Strip **3**

Label for Möbius Strip **4**

THE SQUARE
ROTATING RING

3

3

10

THE SQUARE ROTATING RING

The other piece of this model is on page 9.

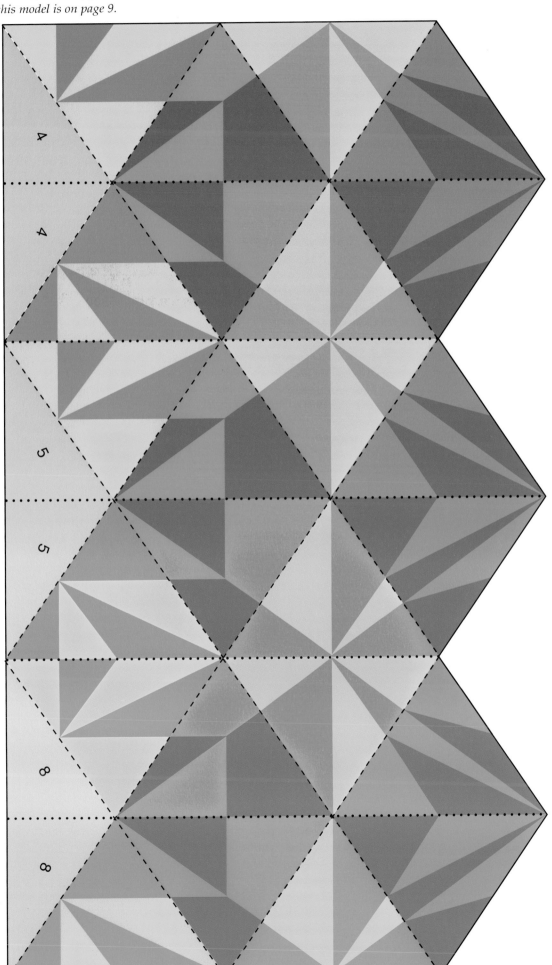

THE SQUARE
ROTATING RING

2

1

4

4

5

5

8

THE FIVE COLOUR TORUS

On a flat surface, or on the surface of a sphere or a cube, it is impossible to arrange five colours so that all of them touch the other four. However, on a torus it can be done and this curious model shows how. See also pages 12 & 13 of the minibook.

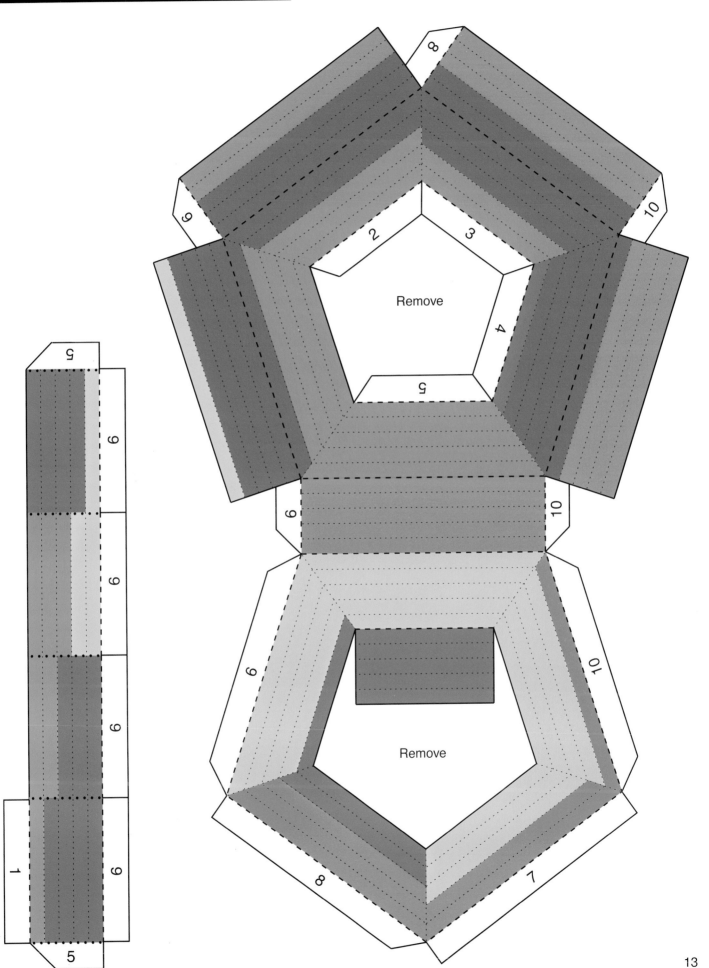

8

7

8

10

6

1

10

6

4

10

9

3

5

5

9

5

6

2

9

9

A collection of interesting and curious models of a mathematical nature

This curious rotating model has been coloured with seven colours so that each of them touches the other six. This is the maximum number of colours for which this can be done and contrasts with a maximum of four on a plane. See pages 13 & 14 of the minibook.

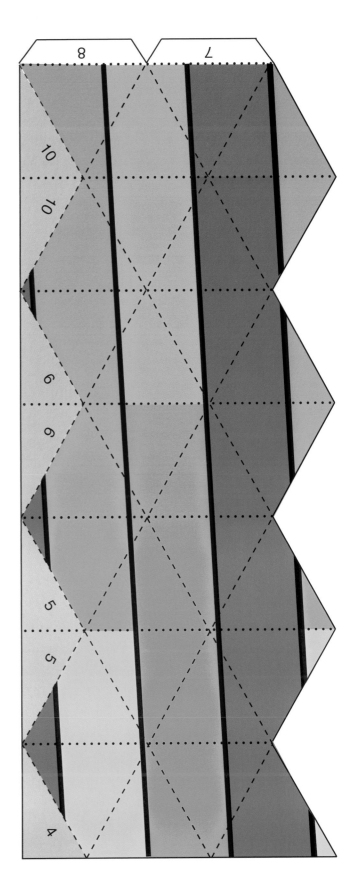

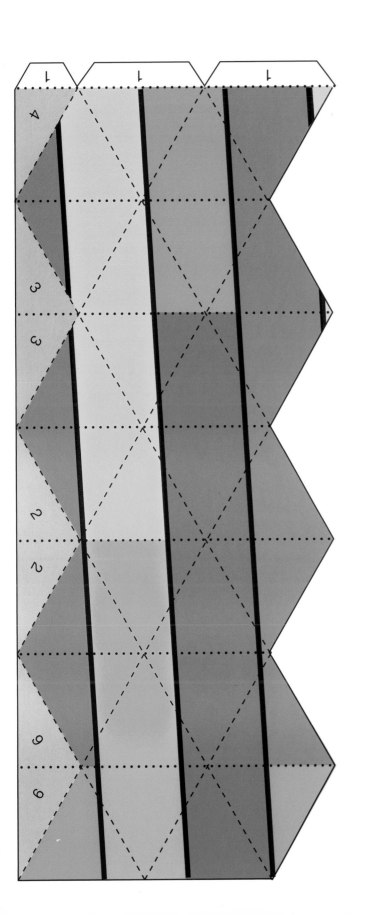

THE SEVEN
COLOUR RING

10

10

6

4

3

6

3

5

2

5

2

4

9

1   1   1

9

7   8

PENTAGRAM AND PYRAMID

The other pieces of this model are on page 19.

Two pentagonal pyramids, one of which is dissected, combine to show in a colourful way the relationships between the surfaces. There is more information about this curious combination on page 7 of the minibook.

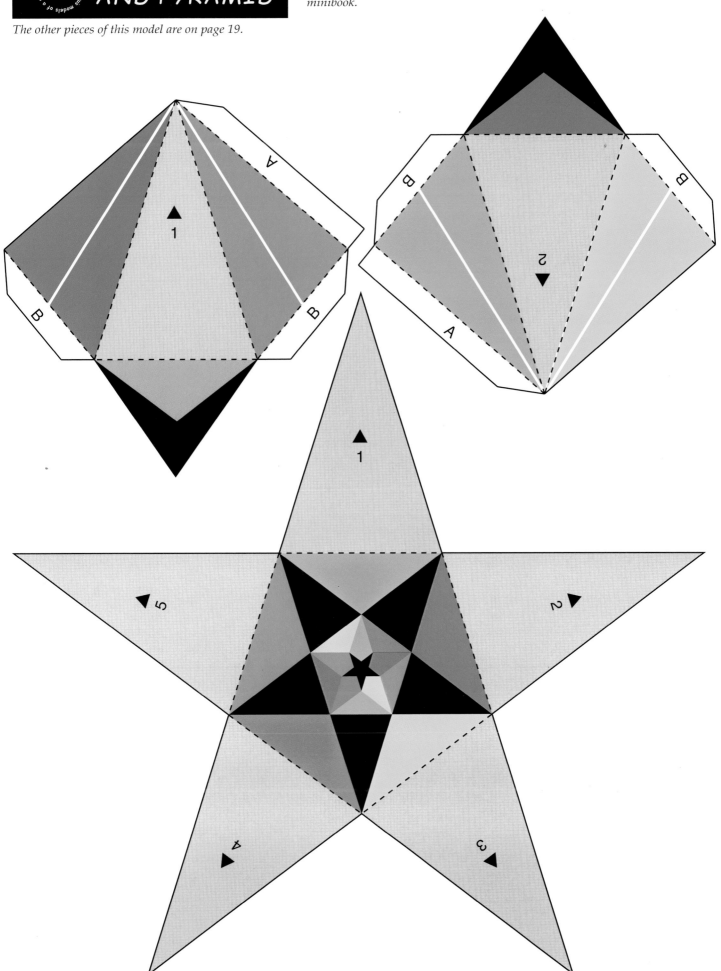

The other pieces of this model are on page 17.

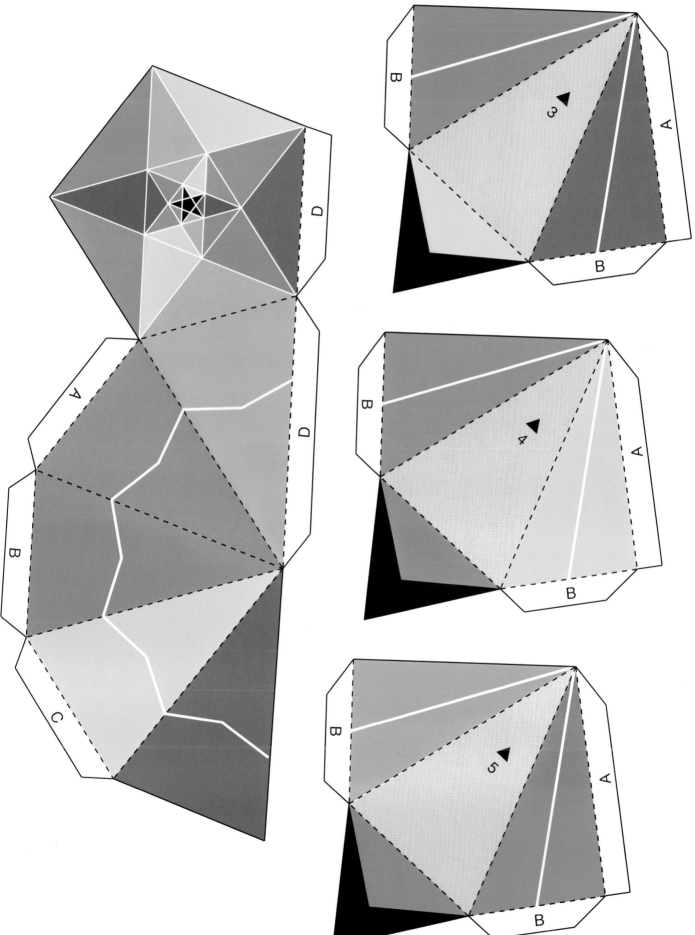

A

C

B

B

B

A

A

B

B

A

D

D

B

B

DUDENEY'S DISSECTION

This clever dissection was first discovered by the great puzzle designer Henry Dudeney and here it is converted into a curious three-dimensional model. Not only does a square transform smoothly into an equilateral triangle, it also changes the sun into the moon! See also page 6 of the minibook.

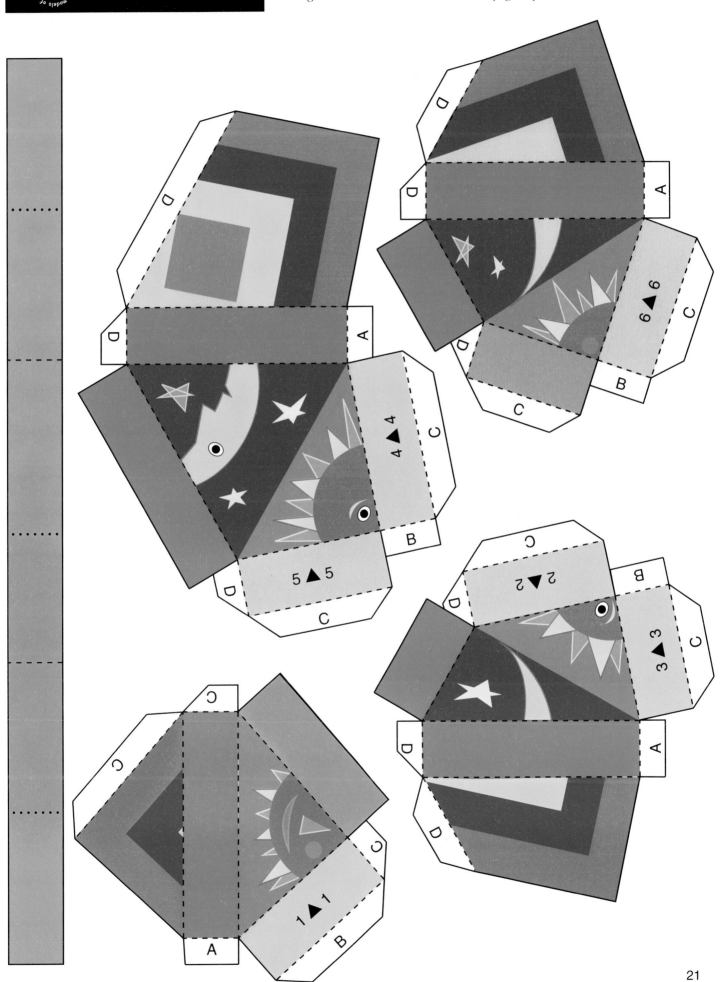

DUDENEY'S
DISSECTION

C

C

A

C

C

D

C

D

D

A

B

D

6 ◄ 6

5 ◄ 5

4 ◄◄ 4

B

D

D

B

D

A

D

D

C

C

3 ◄ 3

2 ◄ 2

C

1 ◄ 1

C

B

A

THE MAGIC CUBE

This curious model shows a 3 x 3 x 3 magic cube which uses all of the numbers 1 to 27 once each. It also opens to reveal the middle slice making it possible to see inside and check that the rows, columns and some diagonals all add up to 42. For more information, see page 4 of the minibook.

The other piece of this model is on page 25.

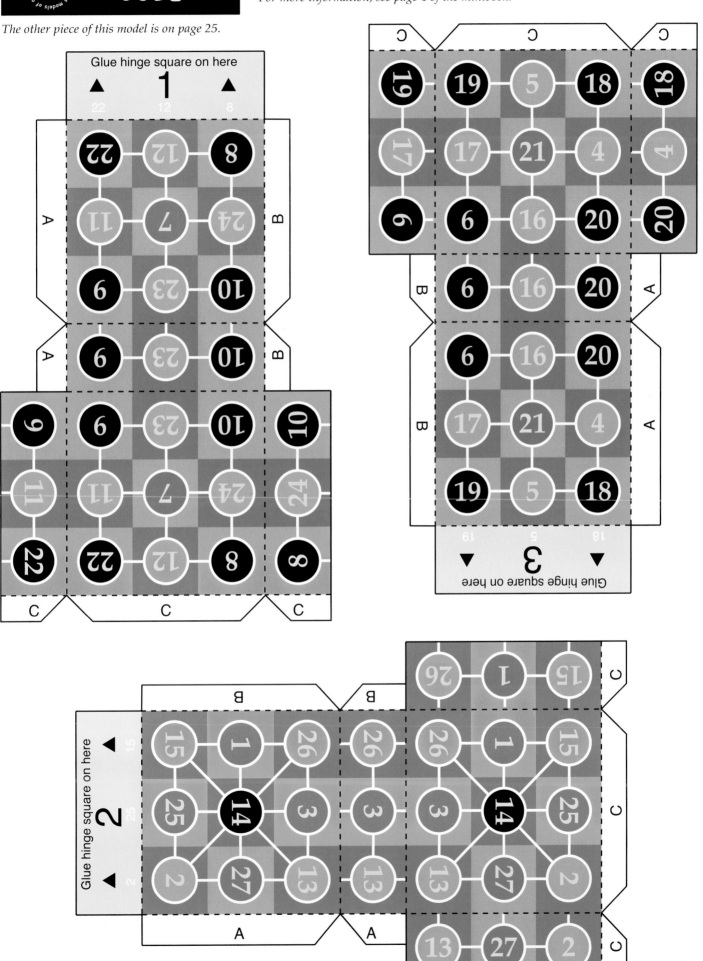

A

A

C

C

C

B

A

B

B

A

B

A

B

C

C

C

B

B

C

C

C

C

A

A

THE MAGIC CUBE

The other pieces of this model are on page 23.

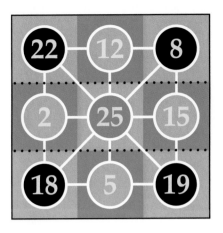

THE GEODESIC SPHERE

The other pieces of this model are on page 27.

This curious model is made from 120 plane triangles and is very close to being a perfect sphere. All the triangles have the same measurements but 60 are black and 60 are white to emphasise that they occur in mirror-image pairs. The red lines represent 15 great circles which are symmetrically arranged around the model. For further information, see pages 10 & 11 of the minibook.

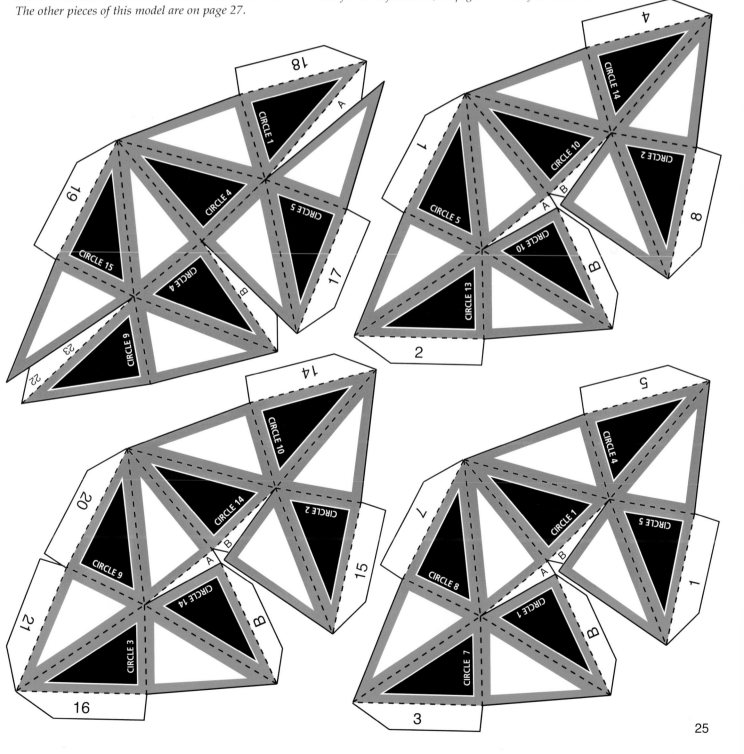

THE MAGIC CUBE

▲ **1** ▲
▲ **2** ▲
▲ **3** ▲

THE GEODESIC SPHERE

8

4

17

18

B

B

1

B

2

23

23

20

21

15

14

1

5

B

B

4

B

16

3

26

The other pieces of this model are on page 25.

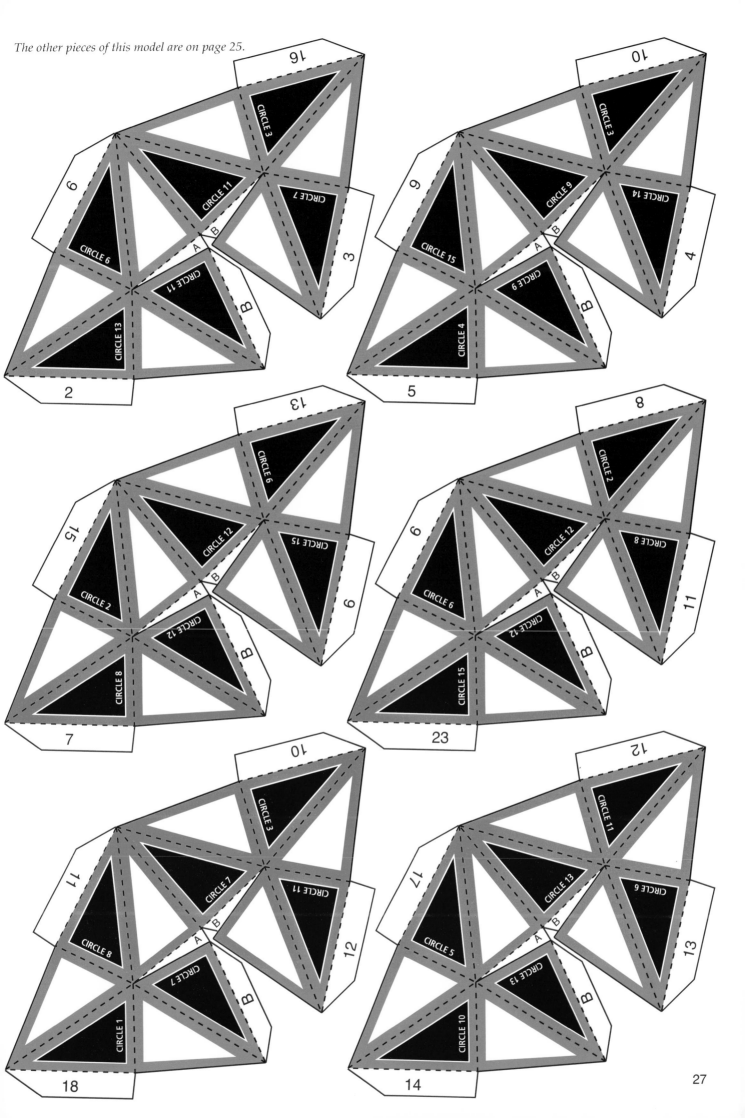

4

10

3

16

B

b

A

B

b

A

6

6

5

2

11

8

6

13

B

b

A

B

b

A

6

15

19

7

22

13

12

12

10

B

b

A

B

b

A

17

11

14

18

28